For my children Nadim and Adia – you are truly
gifts from God.

Published by Sacred Square Publishing Australia
sacredsquarepublishing.com
info@sacredsquarepublishing.com

First Published 2004
This edition published 2020

 A catalogue record for this
work is available from the
National Library of Australia

NATIONAL
LIBRARY
OF AUSTRALIA

ISBN: 978 0 6485851 2 1 (pbk)

Cover design by Lusya Stetskovych

A Gift From God

Written by Tahirih Lemon
Illustrated by Lusya Stetskovych

SACRED
Square
Publishing

Adia was always asking questions.

"Why is the ocean blue?"

"Where does the wind come from...

...and where does it go?"

Adia was particularly curious about
the person referred to as God.

"You're a gift from
God,"
her mother said.

"Was I wrapped in shiny
paper and ribbons?"

A gift from God
• Adia •

"No!" laughed Adia's mother. "Your name actually means 'a gift from God'."

"Who is God? When do I get to meet Him?" asked Adia.

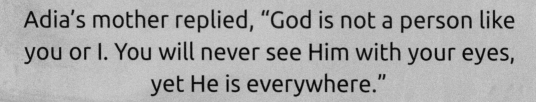

Adia's mother replied, "God is not a person like you or I. You will never see Him with your eyes, yet He is everywhere."

"You can't see God because He is so much greater than you or I..."

...but you can talk to Him anytime you like. He is always listening," said Adia's mother. "People often talk to God when they need help, or when they are sad."

"Do you know God's phone number?"
asked Adia, "I would like to talk to God."

"You don't need a phone to talk to God,"
replied Adia's mother. "God listens to
people's hearts."

"The best way to talk to God is through our prayers."
"I can't wait to talk to God. I have so many things I need to tell Him!" exclaimed Adia.

A Jewish Prayer

Hear, O Israel, the Lord is our God, the Lord is One.
Blessed be the name of the glory of His kingdom
forever and ever.
You shall love the Lord your God with all your heart, with all
your soul, and with all your might. And these words which I
command you today shall be upon your heart.

A Hindu Prayer

Om, May we all be protected.
May we all be nourished.
May we work together with great energy.
May our intellect be sharpened (may our study be effective).
Let there be no animosity amongst us.
Om, peace (in me), peace (in nature), peace (in divine forces).

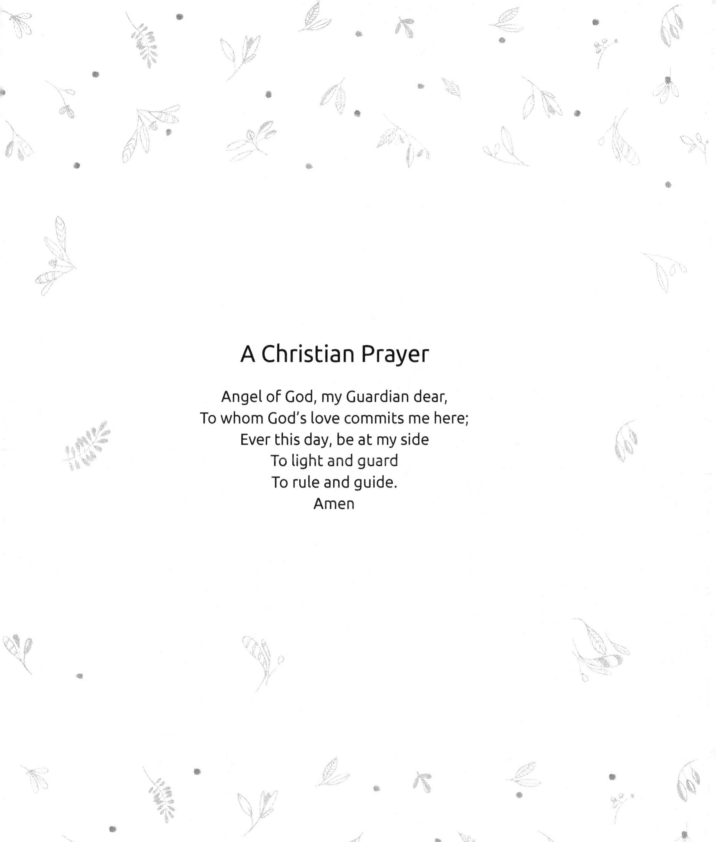

A Christian Prayer

Angel of God, my Guardian dear,
To whom God's love commits me here;
Ever this day, be at my side
To light and guard
To rule and guide.
Amen

A Muslim Prayer

In Thy name, Lord, I lay me down and in Thy name will I rise up... O God, Thou art the first and before Thee there is nothing; Thou art the last and after Thee there is nothing; Thou art the outmost and above Thee there is nothing; Thou art the inmost and below Thee there is nothing... Waken me, O God, in the hour most pleasing to Thee and use me in the works most pleasing to Thee, that Thou mayest bring me ever nearer to Thyself.

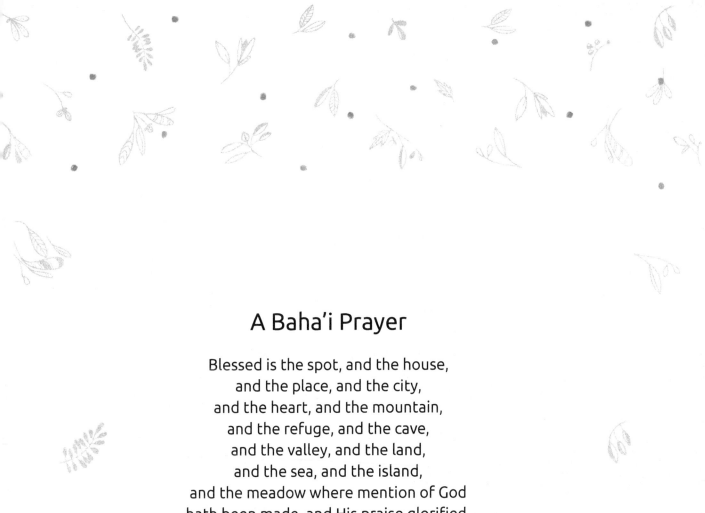

A Baha'i Prayer

Blessed is the spot, and the house,
and the place, and the city,
and the heart, and the mountain,
and the refuge, and the cave,
and the valley, and the land,
and the sea, and the island,
and the meadow where mention of God
hath been made, and His praise glorified.